P9-CRE-075

Animal World

We use information to understand the interdependence of people and animals.

ISBN 0-590-49119-9

2 3 4 5 6 7 8 9 10 23 02 01 00 99 98 97 96

Learn at a Zoo

We use information
to understand
the interdependence
of people and animals.

Animals and Us

Animals and people work together.

SECTION 2

Helping Hands

Some people study and work with animals.

SECTION 3

Save the Animals

We can help endangered animals.

Trade Books

The following books accompany this *Animal World* SourceBook.

Humorous Fiction

A Place for Grace

by Jean Davies Okimoto
illustrated by Doug Keith

Nonfiction

Kitten Care and Critters, Too!

by Judy Petersen-Fleming
and Bill Fleming
illustrated by Debra
Reingold-Reiss

Nonfiction

Who Eats What?

by Patricia Lauber
illustrated by Holly Keller

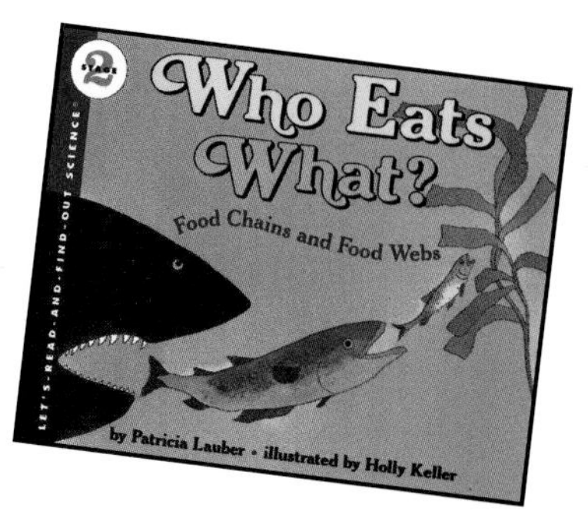

Big Book

Fiction

Antarctica

by Helen Cowcher

Animals and Us

Animals and people work together.

Find out some surprising ways in which people and animals may need each other.

Share the adventure of a dog whose courage saved many lives. Then learn how another dog helps people feel better.

SOURCE

Environmental Fiction

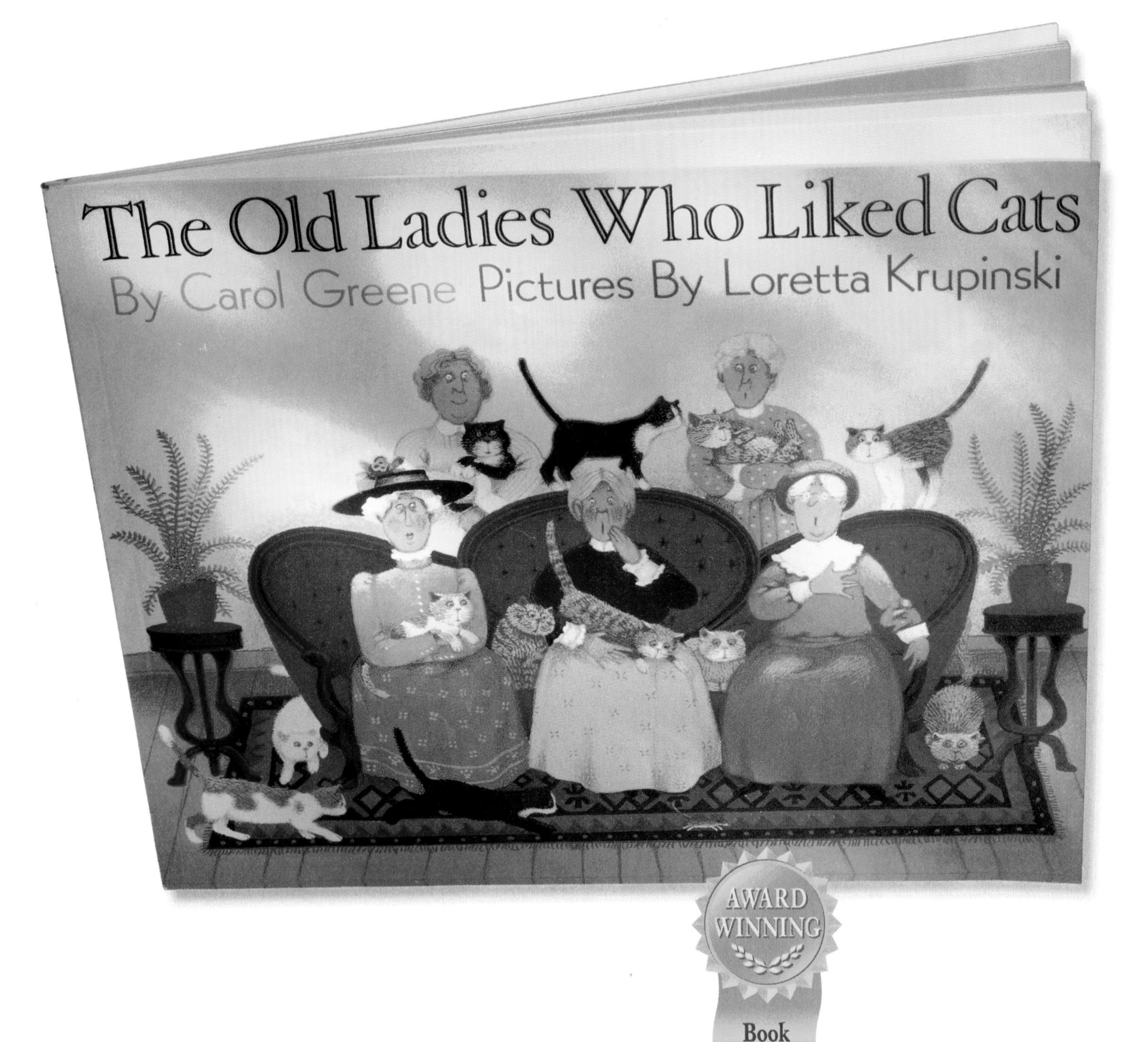

Once there was an island with a town in the center,

and beyond the town grew fields of sweet red clover,
and beyond the fields stretched a dark green forest,
all the way to the sea,

and on the sea sailed the navy, round and round the island, keeping it safe.

Now, the sailors in the navy were strong and healthy because they drank plenty of good fresh milk that came from the cows in the fields,

and the cows gave the good fresh milk
because they ate plenty of sweet red clover,

and the clover grew thick
because long-tongued bees carried pollen from blossom to blossom,

and the bees carried pollen
because there were no field mice to eat their honeycombs,

and there were no field mice
because cats from town chased them into the forest,

and the cats chased the mice because the old ladies who liked cats let them out each night and said, "Chase those mice and keep our island safe!" (They were wise old ladies, you see, and knew how things work together.)

But late one night, the mayor of the town went for a walk, tripped over a cat, and fell flat on his face in a puddle.

"I shall make a new law!" he cried. "From now on, cats must stay inside at night. That will keep our island safe."

The old ladies who liked cats sighed and shook their heads, but they kept their cats inside at night,

and the cats couldn't chase the field mice,
and the field mice ate the honeycombs,

and the long-tongued bees stopped carrying pollen,

and the clover grew thin and sour,

and the cows gave poor milk,

and the sailors became weak and sickly,

and one night invaders came.

They sailed right past the navy, swarmed through the forest, trampled over the fields, stomped into the town, and shouted, "This is our island now!"

In the days that followed, they ate everything in sight, littered the streets, frightened the children, and took up all the room.

"What shall we do?" cried the townsfolk.

"What shall we do?" cried the mayor.

"This is what you must do," said the old ladies who liked cats. (They were wise old ladies, you'll remember, and knew how things work together.) "You must change your law and let our cats out at night. Then the island will be safe again."

The mayor scratched his head. "Imagine that!" he said. "All right. The law is changed."

So out came the cats that chased the field mice,

and away ran the mice and left the honeycombs,

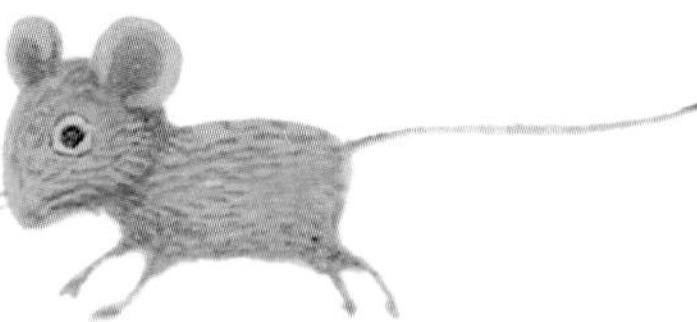

and back came the long-tongued bees that carried the pollen,

and up grew the clover, thick and sweet,

and the cows ate plenty and gave good fresh milk,

and the sailors drank plenty and became strong and healthy,

and one day they threw the invaders off the island.

"Well done!" said the mayor, and pinned medals on them all.

But the sailors took them off and gave them to the real heroes...
the old ladies who liked cats.

From Scholastic's

The Magic School Bus™

ON THE OCEAN FLOOR

by Joanna Cole
illustrated by Bruce Degen

SOURCE

Nonfiction

Plankton plants make food by using energy from the sun. Plankton animals eat the plankton plants. Larger animals eat the plankton animals. This is called a **food chain**. Without the sun shining on plankton plants most ocean animals could not exist.

SOURCE
Nonfiction

BALTO
The Dog Who Saved Nome
By Margaret Davidson
Illustrated by Cathie Bleck
SCHOLASTIC
AWARD WINNING
Author

“THIS IS NOME, ALASKA. REPEAT. THIS IS NOME, ALASKA. WE NEED HELP. FAST...”

A man bent over the machine in the Nome telegraph office. Again and again he pressed down the signal key. *Click-click-clack . . . Clack-click-clack . . .* He was sending a message to the town of Anchorage, Alaska, 800 miles to the south.

Click-click-clack . . . Clack-click-clack . . . The Anchorage telegraph operator wrote down the message.
The news was very bad.

A terrible sickness had broken out in the Nome area—a disease called diphtheria. Some people had already died of it. Many more would die if they weren't treated soon.

There was no medicine to treat diphtheria in Nome. The medicine they needed would have to come from Anchorage—800 miles away—through a wild wind and snow storm. The storm was so bad that airplanes couldn't fly through it. Trains couldn't get through either. Nome was very near the sea, but the sea was frozen solid. And the road from the south was completely blocked by deep drifts of snow.

There was only one way to get the medicine from Anchorage to Nome—by dogsled.

The medicine was packed in a box and sent north by train—as far as a train could go on the snowy tracks. It was still more than 600 miles south of Nome. From now on teams of dogs would have to take it the rest of the way.

The teams were ready. The first team pushed north through the storm to a little town. There a second team was waiting. It went on to another small town where a third team was ready to take the medicine on north.

At first the teams managed to go many miles before they grew tired. But the storm was growing worse by the minute. Finally Charlie Olson's team staggered into the little village of Bluff—60 miles south of Nome. They had only gone 20 miles, yet Olson and the dogs were almost frozen and completely worn out.

Gunnar Kasson and his team were waiting in Bluff. The wind screamed through the little town. The snow was piling up deeper and deeper on the ground. It was 30 degrees *below* zero Fahrenheit outside now. And the temperature was falling fast.

"It's no use trying to go out in *that,*" Charlie Olson said. "I almost didn't make it. You and the dogs will freeze solid before you get half way."

But Kasson knew how important the medicine was. He knew that hundreds—maybe thousands—of people would die if they didn't get the medicine soon. Besides, he knew he didn't have to go all the way. Another team was waiting 40 miles north in the little village of Safety. That team would take the medicine the last 20 miles to Nome.

Quickly Gunnar Kasson hitched up his team of dogs. And at the head of the long line he put his lead dog, Balto.

Balto was a mixed-breed. He was half Eskimo dog—and half wolf. Many dogs who are part wolf never become tame. They never learn to trust people—or obey them either. Balto was different. He was a gentle dog who obeyed orders quickly. He also knew how to think for himself.

Usually Gunnar Kasson guided the dogs. He told them where to go. Now he couldn't even see his hand in front of his face. So everything was up to Balto. The big black dog would have to find the trail by smell. Then he'd have to stay on it no matter what happened.

Gunnar Kasson climbed onto the back of the sled. He cracked his whip in the air. "*Mush!*" he cried. "*Move out!*"

The first part of the trail to Nome led across the sea ice. This ice wasn't anything like ice on a small pond or lake. It seemed much more *alive.* And no wonder. The water *under* the ice was moving up and down because of the storm. So the ice was moving up and down too. Up and down, up and down it went, like a roller coaster.

In some places the ice was smooth—as smooth and slippery as glass. Dogs are usually sure-footed. But they slipped and skidded across this ice. So did the sled.

And sometimes the ice came to sharp points—points that dug deep into the dogs' paws.

Worst of all were the places where the ice was bumpy—so bumpy that the sled turned over again and again. Each time it turned over the other dogs began to bark and snap at each other. But Balto always stood quietly while Kasson set the sled upright again. Balto was calm, so the other dogs grew calmer too.

The team had been moving across the ice for hours.

Suddenly there was a loud *cracking* sound—like a gun going off. Kasson knew that sound. It was the sound of ice breaking. Somewhere not far ahead the ice had split apart. If the team kept going straight they would run right into the freezing water—and drown.

Balto heard the ice crack too. He slowed for a moment. Then he turned left. He headed straight out to sea. He went for a long time. Then he turned right once more.

Balto was leading the team *around* the icy water. Finally he gave a sharp bark and turned north. He had found the trail to Nome again.

Soon the trail left the sea ice. From now on it was over land. Things should have been easier. They weren't. The snow was falling thick and fast. In some places the wind swept most of it off the trail. But in other places the snow drifts came up almost over the dogs' heads. And the wind was blowing harder and harder. It sent bits of icy snow straight into Kasson's eyes. "I might as well have been blind," he said. "I couldn't even *guess* where we were."

And the dogs were so tired! Again and again they tried to stop. They wanted to lie down and go to sleep in the snow. Balto was just as tired. But he would not stop. He kept on pulling—and the other dogs had to follow behind.

Now something else began to worry Gunnar Kasson. They had been traveling for about 14 hours. Surely they should have reached the town of Safety in 14 hours. Kasson went on for another hour. Then he knew. Somehow they had missed the town in the storm. They must have passed right by the new dog team!

Kasson knew they couldn't stop and wait for the storm to die down. He and the dogs would freeze if they did. They couldn't go back to Bluff either. They had come too far. There was only one thing to do now. Pray . . . and push on to Nome.

Later Gunnar Kasson said he couldn't remember those last miles very well. Each one was a nightmare of howling wind and swirling snow and bitter cold. But somehow—with Balto leading slowly and steadily—they made it! At 5:30 in the morning, February 2, 1925—after 20 hours on the trail—the team limped into Nome!

The whole town was waiting for the medicine! They gathered around Gunnar Kasson. They shook his hand and pounded him on the back. "How can we ever thank you?" one woman cried.

Gunnar Kasson shook his head. Then he sank to his knees beside Balto. He began to pull long splinters of ice from the dog's paws. "Balto, what a dog," he said. "I've been in Alaska for 20 years and this was the toughest trip I've ever made. But Balto, *he* brought us through."

Many newspaper and magazine stories were written about Balto. His picture was printed on postcards and in books. And today, on a grassy hill in New York City's Central Park, there is a life-sized statue of Balto—the dog who saved Nome.

Statue of Balto in Central Park
New York City

Photos by JUSTIN SUTCLIFFE

Puppygarten Star

Meet Rosie, an awesome dog with a great job! Rosie visits people. It's her job to help cheer them up.

Paws down, Rosie is a great visiting dog. She is a Tibetan terrier, good-natured and friendly. Those traits gave her a head start. School gave her the skills.

Puppygarten

Rosie's owner, Stephanie Calmenson, took her goofy, playful puppy to kindergarten. There a teacher taught Rosie to "sit," "stay," "lie down" and "come" on command.

Later, Rosie joined a special visiting dog program for advanced training.

Love Knots

Kids Rosie visits like to care for her. This boy, who is blind, enjoys brushing Rosie's fur.

Lap Dog

Rosie makes friends wherever she goes. Thomas likes Rosie, so he doesn't mind her getting comfortable on his lap.

Helping Hands

Some people study and work with animals.

Read a story about how people saved a whale. Then meet some of the real people on the rescue team.

Learn about some special animals all over the world who are in danger.

Find out why the work Lisa Stevens does is so important to so many animals.

IBIS
A True Whale Story
by John Himmelman
SCHOLASTIC
AWARD WINNING
Book

Deep in a bay,
off the coast of an old fishing village,
lived a pod of humpback whales.

One of the whales
was a little calf named Ibis.
Ibis was curious about everything in the ocean.

One day she and her friend Blizzard
went out swimming. They saw many kinds of fish.
The most interesting were the starfish.
Ibis liked to look at them.
There was something about their shape
that made her feel good.

As Ibis and Blizzard were drifting over a reef
they heard a strange humming noise.
The two calves looked up to see something
large and dark pass overhead.
It was as big as a whale,
but it wasn't a whale.

The calves were frightened.
They had never seen a boat before.
They swam back to their mothers.

The next day, Ibis went back to the reef.
It wasn't long before another boat came along.
Again, Ibis was scared. But she was curious, too.
She forced herself to swim to the surface.

In the cool, hazy air, she saw several faces
watching her. They didn't look scary.
In fact, they looked very friendly.
Ibis liked them.

In the months that followed, Ibis and her friends lost their fear of boats. Boats came in many sizes and shapes, and the people in them always seemed to enjoy seeing the little whales.

As Ibis grew up, she learned more about the sea.
She knew what kinds of sharks to avoid,
what food was the tastiest,
and, best of all, where to find the most dazzling starfish.
Ibis never got tired of looking at starfish.

People and their boats became a part of her life.
Whenever a boat passed overhead, she swam to the top to say hello.

One evening, Ibis and Blizzard saw a school of fish swimming around the bottom of a ship.
Maybe there was something good up there to eat.
They went to find out.

Suddenly Ibis was caught in a fishing net!
She fought to get free. But the more she struggled,
the more tangled up she became.

Finally she broke loose, but part of the net
was caught in her mouth and wrapped around her tail.

Blizzard swam off to find help.

Ibis was confused and hurt.
She wanted to get away, far from people
and their boats and nets.
Slowly and painfully she made her way
toward the deep ocean.

Many weeks passed, and Ibis grew very ill.
The net in her mouth made it hard for her to eat.
And every time she went to the surface for air,
the net cut into her tail. But if she didn't
get air every half hour, she would die.

Winter was coming, and it was time for the whales
to move to warmer waters.
But Ibis felt too weak to make the long journey.

Instead she turned back toward the coast.
It was so hard for her to swim,
she could barely keep moving.
Ibis was about to give up.
Then she saw a familiar shape.
It was Blizzard!

Blizzard saw that Ibis needed help.
Gently Blizzard pushed her to the surface
so she could breathe.

Suddenly the water was filled with the sounds
of boat engines.
The whales saw two small rafts
and a boat circling them.

Blizzard and Ibis tried to get away fast.
But Ibis wasn't quick enough.
The boats rushed toward her before she could dive.

The people in the boats began to attach large floats
to the pieces of net that were hurting Ibis.
Blizzard stayed nearby,
circling the boats nervously.

Because of the floats, Ibis could not dive.
She began to panic,
but she did not have the strength to fight.
When the boats came in closer,
a person reached into the water.

Ibis stared at the person's hand.
The hand reminded her of something—
something she loved very much.
She began to feel better.

Soon many hands dipped into the water.
Ibis felt them tugging at the lines of the net.
Moments later the lines fell away, and she was free!

Ibis blew a big spout from her blowhole
as if to say, "Thank you! Thank you!"
Then she dived deep into the water.
For the first time in many weeks, she felt no pain.
She felt wonderful!

Blizzard joined her.
Then the two whales popped back to the surface
for one more look.

The people were waving their starfish-shaped hands.
Ibis knew the hands had helped her,
and that the people were still her friends.

Soon Blizzard and Ibis were leaping and diving
with the other whales, far away in the warm waters
where they would spend the winter together.

SOURCE

Photo Essay

Working With

Dr. Carole Carlson and David Mattila work at the Center for Coastal Studies in Provincetown, Massachusetts. They are just two of the many people who work there.

Some work inside, at desks. Others work outside, on boats. They are all there for one reason. They are all trying to find out about the animals in the ocean, especially about whales.

Whales

Some people from the center go out to sea to gather information. Once the information is gathered, it is put into a computer. It can then be shared with people in other parts of the country.

People who use this information will know how whales live, move, and eat. The people will then be able to help whales if they get into trouble.

Ibis was one of the whales Carlson, Mattila, and their team helped. She was the first whale ever saved that was tangled in a fishing net.

Environmental Nonfiction

from

Will We Miss Them?

Endangered Species

by
Alexandra Wright

illustrated by
Marshall Peck III

Miss Them?

This book is about some amazing animals that are disappearing from the Earth. Some are becoming scarce because hunters kill them for their horns, tusks, skins, or fur. Others are vanishing because they cannot compete with people for space, water, or food. Will we miss these animals? Can we help save them? The first step is to learn who they are.

Will we miss the bald eagle?

The bald eagle is not really bald. It is called bald because from a distance you can't see the white feathers on its head.

Bald eagles build huge nests—five to eight feet wide. When there are no big old trees in peaceful, quiet places, bald eagles have no place to build their nests. Once, bald eagles lived in every state except Hawaii, but now they are thriving only in the state of Alaska and in parts of Canada where there are lots of big trees.

These bald eagles are searching for their dinner. Bald eagles have better eyesight than many other creatures. They can spot small animals from hundreds of feet in the air!

Will we miss the African elephant?

African elephants are the largest creatures on land. Their babies weigh more than grown-up people do! The elephant's trunk is really an upper lip and nose. The muscles on the top of the trunk are very strong and can be used for pushing. The underside is much more delicate.

You will never see an elephant striking a blow with its trunk because that would hurt. The trunk is not used as a drinking straw, either. The elephant takes water up into its trunk and then squirts it into its mouth.

Elephants are endangered because of two problems—hunters and farmers. As more people try to farm the land, there is less space for the elephants. Also, hunters kill elephants for their valuable ivory tusks. You can help protect elephants by refusing to buy anything made of ivory.

Will we miss the panda?

The panda lives in only a few small areas of China, in places where plenty of bamboo grows. Pandas will eat small rodents and several kinds of plants, but their favorite food is bamboo. This panda may eat up to forty pounds of bamboo each day. For hours it happily chomps on bamboo shoots. Bamboo splinters don't bother the panda because its throat has a lining that protects it from splinters.

In this picture, the pandas look cute and cuddly, but they are actually quite big and have coarse fur. A full-grown panda may weigh up to 300 pounds.

Pandas have been hunted and have been unable to survive when the bamboo forests died or were cut down. China has passed laws to protect the panda, and pandas are now a worldwide symbol of conservation.

Will we miss the whooping crane?

As winter approaches, the whooping crane flies south to the salt marshes of the Texas Gulf Coast. Its 2,000 mile journey from Canada is full of dangers. It must avoid hungry wolves and coyotes, hunters' guns, power lines, and strong winds.

The whooping crane nearly became extinct. In 1941, only 21 of these large, white cranes were still alive. Then laws were passed to ban all shooting of whooping cranes and to protect their nesting grounds. These laws have helped to save the bird from extinction.

By 1990, people counted 150 whooping cranes, including full-grown birds and their cinnamon-colored babies.

Will we miss the grizzly bear?

Grizzlies like to live in places that make good farms, like open meadows and river valleys. This means that they often compete with people for space and food. Grizzlies eat almost anything—berries, leaves, small animals, fish, or even roots. Grizzlies who live on the West Coast enjoy feasting on salmon in the summer.

In winter, a grizzly finds a cave or a hollow log to use as a den for a long winter sleep. Kitten-sized cubs are born in the winter and are already bigger than a basketball when they leave the den with their mother in the spring. In the United States, except for Alaska, few grizzlies remain. The best place to see one is in the national parks, where they are protected.

Will we miss the manatee?

Manatees are air-breathing mammals. Some scientists think they are related to elephants. Even though manatees are huge, they are playful and peaceful animals. They swim by moving their tails up and down and using their flippers to steer. In shallow water, manatees can "walk" on their flippers. Sometimes they even use their flippers to hug each other!

Manatees live in the warm waters of southern rivers. When they come to the surface to breathe, they are in danger. They are too slow to swim out of the way of motorboats. Many are killed when boats hit them. Others make the mistake of trying to live in the warm streams that come from power plants. If the power plants break down, the manatees catch cold and die unless they find another source of warm water.

Will we miss the rhinoceros?

The name rhinoceros may sound kind of funny, but it means "nose horn." The horn on the rhino's nose grows… and grows—as much as 3 inches a year. The rhinoceros is the only animal that has a horn growing from its nose. Other animals have horns growing on the tops or sides of their heads. A mother rhinoceros uses her horn to protect her baby from lions, hyenas, and crocodiles.

There are five kinds of rhinos. Some have only one horn, others have two. But all rhinos have very poor eyesight and must drink water often. That makes them easy to hunt. It is against the law to kill rhinos, but hunters still kill them for their horns, which are very valuable. There are now very few rhinos left, and most of them live in protected reserves.

Will we miss the mountain gorilla?

The mountain gorilla is the largest living primate. This gentle, shy creature is the only ape that likes to spend most of its time on the ground instead of in the trees. It eats seeds, fruit, nettles, wild celery, thistles, and other plants. With an opposable thumb like humans have, these apes can pick up the smallest seeds. Only a few hundred mountain gorillas are still alive. They live in a few small areas of central Africa, where they are studied and protected.

You might see a lowland gorilla in a zoo, but a mountain gorilla can only live if it is free. A group of mountain gorillas is led by a large, silverbacked male. He protects the group and leads it through the forest. Newborn babies weigh about $4\frac{1}{2}$ pounds. Their mothers and aunts feed and carry them, and shelter them in a nest of branches at night. Just like people, their babies can't walk until they are about one year old.

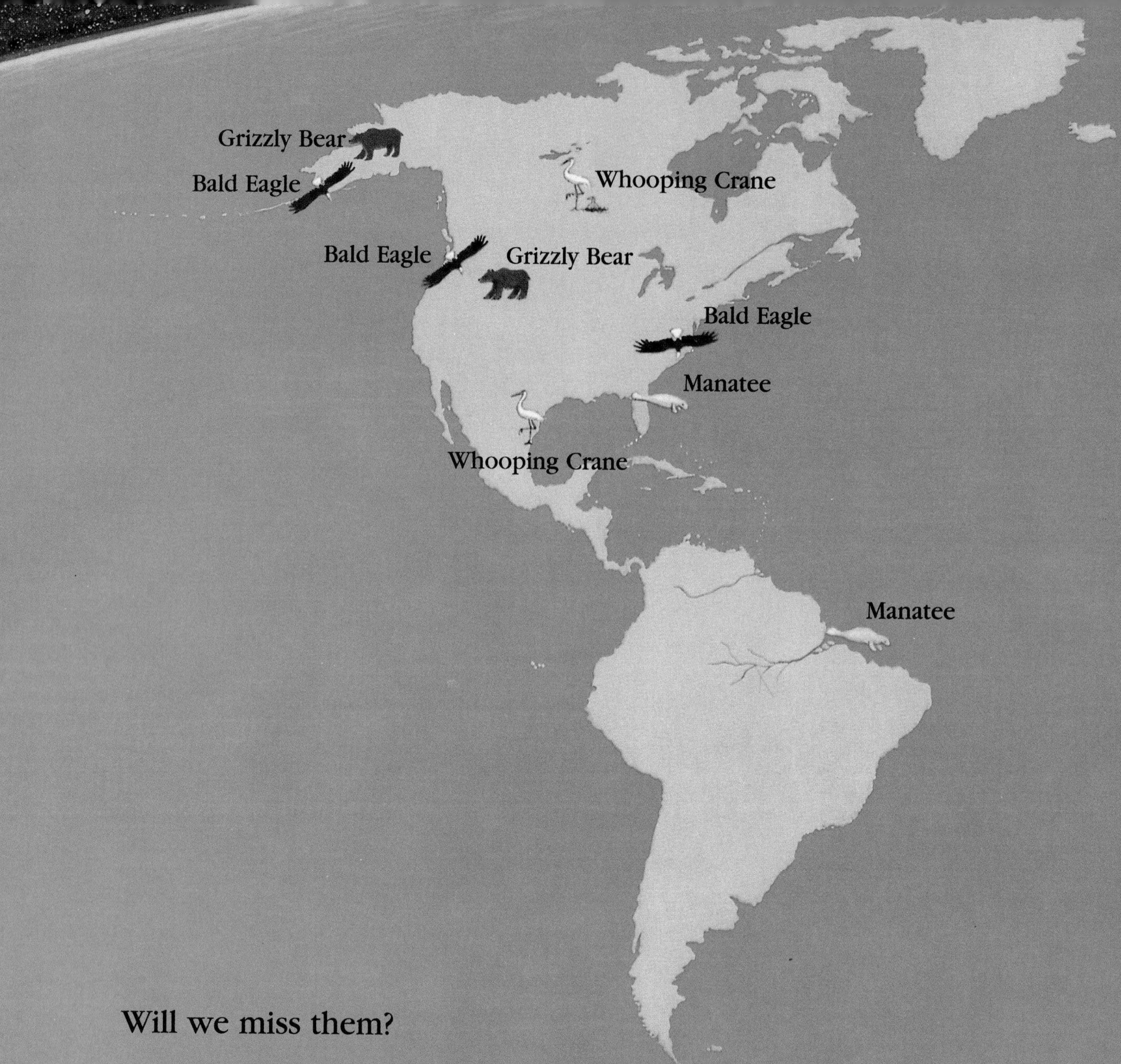

Will we miss them?

Yes, we probably will. Each animal is part of a pattern that is woven into everyone's life.

But we don't have to miss them. We still have time to save these endangered animals. We can save them because, like the whooping crane, they are beautiful. We can save them because, like the grizzly bear, they are an important part of our heritage. We can save them for the most important reason of all—they are all part of the amazing balance of nature that makes life so wonderful.

Protection of wildlife is very important now because so many species are endangered. Millions of wild animals are killed every year to supply people with fur coats, souvenirs, and exotic pets. Special habitats such as salt marshes are destroyed by pollution. Rain forests are cut down for their wood and to make more space for farms, homes, and industry.

To help endangered species, learn everything you can about them, and tell other people about them. Visit the zoo and your local library to find out about wild animals in your area. No matter where you live, you can do something. If we all care, we can make our world a place where people and animals can live together in harmony.

MENTOR

Lisa Stevens

Zoo Curator

please don't feed the zoo animals
AMERICAN ASSOC OF ZOO KEEPERS

Do you like to go to the ZOO?
Some people go EVERY DAY!

Lisa Stevens is a curator of mammals at the National Zoo in Washington, D.C. She is in charge of many keepers, who take care of a giant panda, two camels, and over fifty apes and monkeys.

Lisa Stevens also talks to many visitors at the zoo. She talks about the animals and about protecting them.

Animal Care Staff

Questions

for Lisa Stevens

Here's how zoo curator Lisa Stevens works with her staff to care for animals.

Q **What do you do to help the animals every day?**

A I check to see that they are fed the right foods and are kept active. I make sure they have everything they need to be healthy.

Q **Have you had a problem recently with an animal?**

A Not too long ago, Hsing-Hsing, our panda, developed an eye infection. If we hadn't treated it, he could have gone blind. We found a way to put special eye drops in his eyes to fight the infection.

How did you learn about the different animals?

I learned a lot of what I know on the job. I talked to all the keepers who worked with the animals before me. I looked at the records that are kept on each animal. I also went to the library and read as much as I could about the animals.

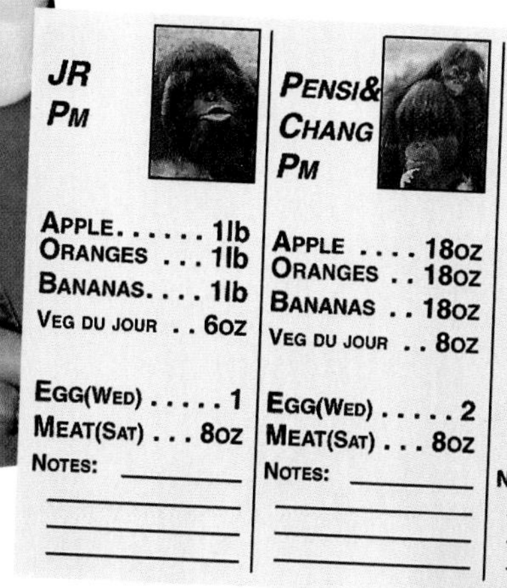

JR PM	PENSI & CHANG PM	PYGMY MARMOSETS PM
APPLE. 1lb	APPLE 18OZ	*1/8 CAN OF MARMOSET DIET
ORANGES . . . 1lb	ORANGES . . 18OZ	*1/8 APPLE
BANANAS. . . . 1lb	BANANAS . . 18OZ	*1/8 ORANGE
VEG DU JOUR . . 6OZ	VEG DU JOUR . . 8OZ	*1/8 BANANA
EGG(WED) 1	EGG(WED) 2	*4 GRAPES
MEAT(SAT) . . . 8OZ	MEAT(SAT) . . . 8OZ	*15 MEALWORMS
NOTES:	NOTES:	NOTES:

Lisa Stevens's Tips for Helping Endangered Animals

1. Learn about animals.
2. Recycle. Don't pollute or waste water. If we save the earth, we help animals that need a place to live.
3. Support your local zoo.

Save the Animals

We can help endangered animals.

Find out how a woman brought the monkeys she loved back to her mountain. Then help some other monkeys find their way through a maze.

Learn how three kids found very different ways to help animals. Then watch a children's game that shows how people can make a better world.

SOURCE

Realistic Fiction

When Doña Marta was a very little girl, the valley was a peaceful place. Children giggled as they chased each other between rows of tall corn. Fathers whistled as they dug in the gardens. Mothers hummed softly as they wrapped black beans and cornmeal in banana leaves to cook.

There was one old road in the valley, but it was an ox-cart road, an open place for meeting friends or cousins, a nice place for walking, a sunny place for catching lizards. There weren't any cars at all. The valley was a quiet place, except when the monkeys called.

Every morning and every evening for as long as anyone could remember, the monkeys announced the changing of night into day, the changing of day into night. At dawn they would howl and bark to one another, and the noise they made was like thunder in the trees. At dusk they would hoot and scream, and each leaf and each blade of grass would tremble from the sound.

One day a car chugged and sputtered up the old road. After that more cars came, not many at first, for the road was an ox road, not a car road. Marta was afraid of the cars. The sound and smell made her hide behind her mother's skirt. More and more cars came, and trucks, and more noise. Before long it wasn't safe to walk down the middle of the road, to stand and talk, to chase the quick lizards.

Still the monkeys shouted from the trees, drowning out all the new noises for a few moments each day, hooting to one another as they always had, waking up the world in the morning, calling the workers home from the fields at night.

The rains came and went and Marta's dress grew too short, and one day some men from the city came to Marta's house. They offered her father a lot of money, enough to buy six cows *and* a brand new dress for Marta, and asked to cut down some trees on the side of the mountain. Marta's father agreed and from that day on, the forest began to disappear.

At first it was just a few trees. The lumbermen cut down only the biggest trees, the ones with the hanging vines. The monkeys didn't seem to mind. They howled and barked and scolded just as before. But five years later, when there were only twenty-four trees left in the forest, the monkeys went away.

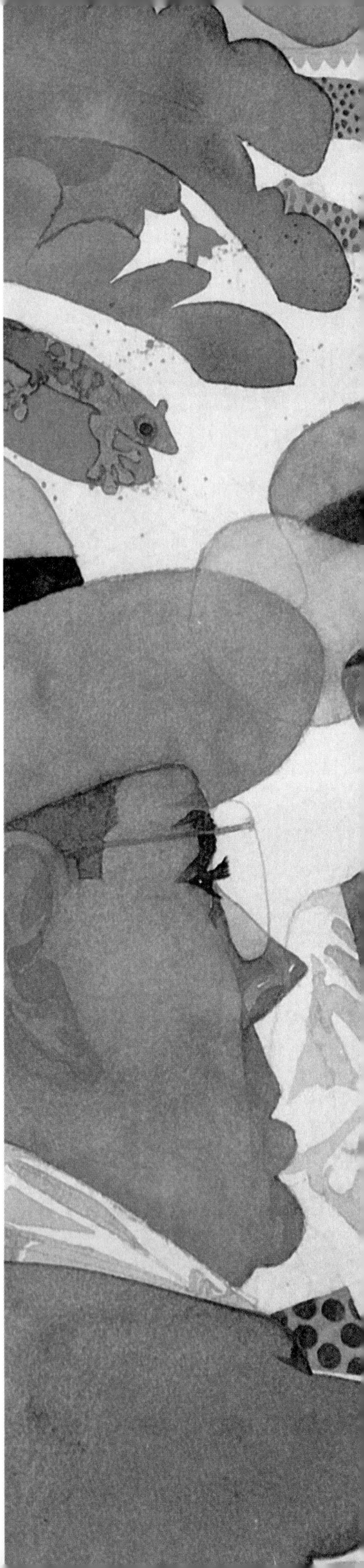

Marta didn't know where the monkeys went. One night, just as the sun slipped behind the hills, the monkeys shrieked and hooted and cried, louder than ever before. Some said it was because of the full moon. Others said the rainy season was near. But the next morning the valley was as silent as a stone.

Over the next several years the last of the trees was cut down. What had once been a forest was now covered with stumps and tangled brush. There were a few birds but no monkeys.

Most people forgot about the monkeys. They had roosters to wake them up in the morning, lamps to work by at night. But Marta didn't forget.

When she was fifteen years old Marta married Emilio. Emilio worked for Marta's father and when her father died, he left his farm to Marta and Emilio.

"You have a lot of land now," said Marta one day. "I would like to have some of it for myself." Emilio laughed out loud, because in those days, women did not own land.

"Soon we will have a family to feed," said Emilio. "After I plant corn and beans and squash, there will be nothing left over to give you. The rest of the land belongs to the cows."

"What about the land on the side of the mountain?" asked Marta. "There are too many stumps for a garden. And it is too steep for cows."

"That's true," agreed Emilio, and though it went against the custom, he gave the land on the side of the mountain to Marta.

"What are you going to do with your land?" asked Emilio.

"I'm going to bring back the forest," said Marta, and that is what she did.

Marta planted trees from the foot of the mountain to as far up as she could climb. When the sun baked the ground in the dry season, she hauled buckets of water to the trees. When the hard rains washed the little trees from the soil, she gently replanted them.

Year after year, Marta took care of the trees. In the next fifteen years she gave birth to eleven children. Each child learned to plant and tend trees. Year after year, Marta's children grew tall and so did the trees.

"Coffee grows well on a mountain," Emilio would tease. "Maybe you could plant coffee on your land." But Marta didn't listen. She didn't change her mind, and the forest came back.

SAN

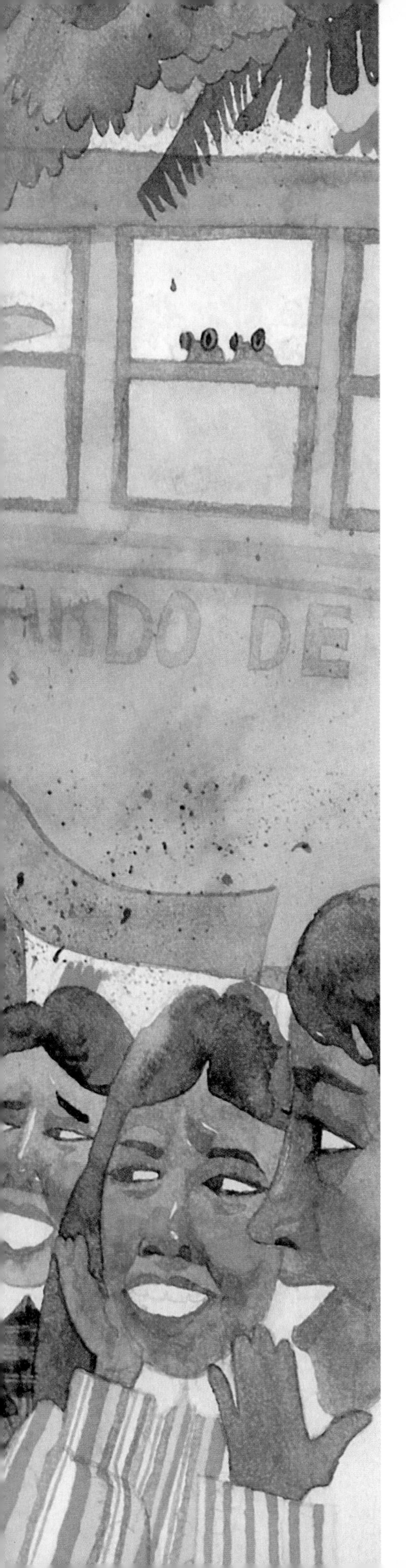

Many more years passed. The trees grew higher and higher. Marta's children grew up and had children of their own. Emilio died and left the farm to Marta and her sons.

One day old Doña Marta took a walk along the road in the warm sunshine. The children greeted her as she passed.

"Good morning, Tree Lady," they said.

"Good morning," answered Doña Marta with a wink and an old, old smile. She leaned on her stick and stared across the valley.

Her trees touched the sky. Thick vines wrapped around their trunks. Birds of every color filled their branches. Now, wherever they dropped their seeds, new trees would grow. The valley was bright with squash and corn and beans, but the side of the mountain was a deep, dark green, forest green. Doña Marta's work was finished.

One night, Doña Marta couldn't sleep. As she lay in her bed she listened to the sounds of insects, the twittering of the night birds. Out her little window she watched the stars trail across the black sky. She watched the moon shadows shift and change in her room. As dawn approached, she heard the roosters begin to crow. And then she heard another sound.

At first it sounded like the barking of dogs, but soon the barking turned into howling, the howling into shrieks, the shrieks into shouts, and every leaf and every blade of grass trembled with the sound. Doña Marta hobbled to the window and leaned out.

The dark air thundered with the sound of monkeys hooting, howling, screaming from the treetops, waking up the whole world once again. Doña Marta closed her eyes, smiled a wrinkled smile, and listened to the music she had missed for fifty-six long years.

Every morning now, old Doña Marta wakes up to the barking and scolding of the monkeys. Every evening she waits for them to gather in the trees to shriek and howl and say good night. For a few moments each morning and evening, the sound of the monkeys drowns out all the other sounds in the valley. For a few moments each day, it's as if nothing had ever changed.

From ANIMAZE!

In the Jungle

By WENDY MADGWICK Illustrated by LORNA HUSSEY

Deep within the rain forest of South America, a group of squirrel monkeys are climbing through the treetops. Below them they spy the juicy, golden fruits of the guava tree. But how can they reach the fruit without disturbing the other creatures of the forest?

Follow the maze of large branches that lead to the fruit, but be careful—it won't be easy, and only one route is safe.

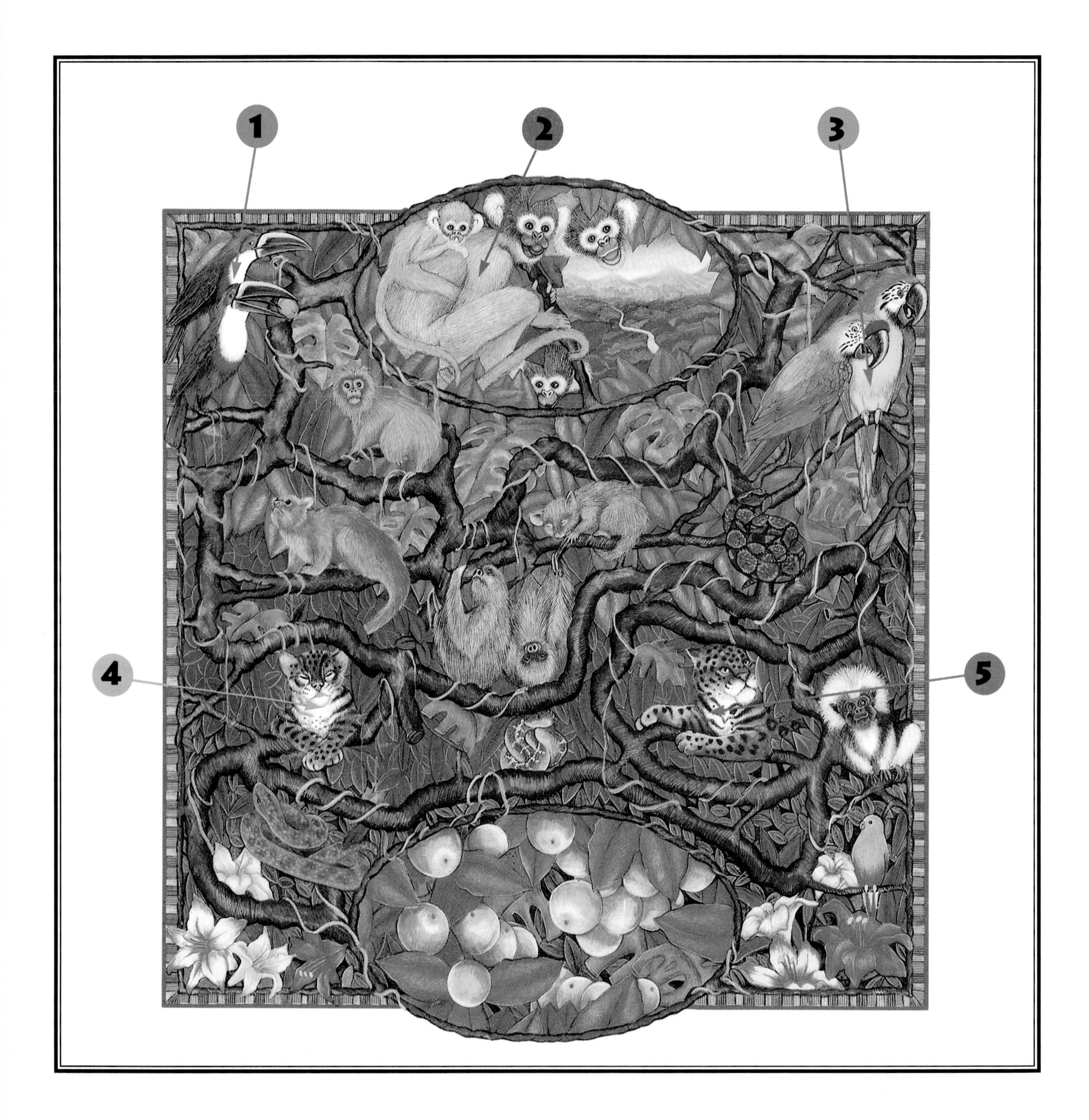
1
2
3
4
5

1 TOUCANS

The toucan's bill is huge but light because its bony tissue is filled with air bubbles. Toucans pick up fruit with their long bills. Then, with a flick of the head, they toss the fruit into their mouths.

2 SQUIRREL MONKEYS

These agile monkeys use their long prehensile (grasping) tails to grip the branches as they travel through the rain forest. Newborn babies hitch a ride on their mother's back.

3 MACAWS

These brilliantly colored birds, members of the parrot family, live in noisy, screeching flocks. They feed on fruits, nuts, and seeds—their strong beaks can even crack the hard shells of Brazil nuts!

4 OCELOT

The ocelot, prized for its beautiful coat, is one of the many small cats threatened with extinction. It usually hunts at night for small mammals, birds, and reptiles. During the day it sleeps, safely hidden among the foliage.

5 JAGUAR

The largest cat of the New World, the jaguar is a powerful hunter. It usually hunts on the ground, but it is an excellent climber and will pursue its prey of monkeys and birds through the trees.

From: **KID HEROES OF THE ENVIRONMENT**

Oliver the Otter

Name: Aruna Chandrasekhar
Age: 9
Grade: 4
Town: Houston, Texas
School: Windsor Village Vanguard Elementary School

Goal: Inform kids about how oil spills affect animals and the environment

What She Did

Summary

In April 1990, Aruna's 4th-grade teacher gave her class an assignment to write a book and enter it in a national writing contest.

Aruna thought, "Here's an opportunity to help children learn about environmental disasters and the importance of preventing them."

She had read about the Exxon *Valdez* oil spill in *National Geographic* magazine and thought kids would want to know how sea creatures were affected by it. She decided to write about otters because "they've been hunted for their coats for many years, and they're almost extinct."

Results

She wrote and illustrated *Oliver and the Oil Spill*, a book about otters trapped in an oil spill off the Pacific Coast. In it, an otter named Oliver and his mother are rescued and have the oil cleaned off their fur. Although his mother dies, Oliver makes it back into the ocean.

The book won first place (out of 7,000 entries) in the 6–9-year-old category; Aruna won a scholarship for $5,000, and the book was published.

How She Did It

1. She did some research to find out what happens to animals in an oil spill, how otters behave, and other facts.
2. She wrote the story, which turned out to be 24 pages. Then she went back and checked it to make sure she liked the way it sounded. It took 6 weeks to finish.
3. She drew pictures for the book.
4. One of her parents typed the story on sheets of white paper. She glued each sheet to a precut cardboard page, then hand-stitched the pages together.
5. She drew a picture for the book cover, added the title, and took it to be "laminated"—covered with clear plastic.

Name: Lyle Solla-Yates
Age: 10
Grade: 5
Town: Miami Shores, Florida
School: Cushman School

Goal: Protect manatees and other endangered species

What He Did

Summary

When Lyle was in first grade, his favorite animals were manatees, rare mammals also known as "sea cows." They live off the coast of Florida.

One day, Lyle read a report in the newspaper about a manatee that had been injured by a motorboat. It made him angry. "I really wanted to do something to help the manatees," he says. So in 1989, he started a group called "Pals of Wildlife" to raise money to help save them.

Results

His group raised hundreds of dollars and has donated the money to various environmental organizations. Lyle says, "We've gotten people to see they can change things. And we learned that helping the environment can be fun!"

How He Did It

1. He called his friends to tell them he was starting the group and when the first meeting would be. About 20 kids joined.

2. At the first meeting, they agreed to support efforts to protect endangered species like panthers and whales, too.

3. They thought of the name "Pals of Wildlife," and a motto: "When the animals die, we're dead meat."

4. They designed T-shirts with their name and motto. Each club member drew a small picture and wrote a slogan to go with it, like "Don't pollute." These were each printed in squares on the T-shirts.

5. To raise money, they sold the T-shirts. In addition, a club member asked a local pencil supplier to print "Pals of Wildlife" on pencils. Then the kids sold the pencils for 25¢ each.

6. They had fund-raisers like an "Earthday Birthday" party, with tree planting, ecology-oriented arts and crafts, and games.

7. For the fund-raisers, each Pal's family handled one job, like bringing "Birthday" cake or coordinating tree planting.

8. They donated the money earned from the fund-raisers to the Children's Rainforest Project and Greenpeace.

BATMAN

Name: Hunter Allen
Age: 8
Grade: 2
Town: Huntington, Massachusetts
School: Murrayfield School

Goal: Find a new home for bats living in the attic of a renovated community building

What He Did

Summary

Hunter had read about bats in *Ranger Rick* magazine. He was fascinated by these night creatures, which frighten people but aren't actually dangerous at all. (In fact, they can eat hundreds of insect pests in one night.)

Then Hunter's mother told him about some bats in the attic of North Hall, a nearby community center that was being restored. (She had seen them while doing electrical wiring in the building.) The problem was, the building maintenance people wanted the bats to move out.

Hunter was concerned that the bats might be killed or have trouble finding a new place to live. Then he remembered that the article in *Ranger Rick* had included instructions for making "bat boxes." So he set out to make some.

Results

The bats have a new home on the side wall of North Hall. It's not clear if they've moved in yet because bats take at least a year to get settled in a new place—but they have a place to go if they need it.

How He Did It

1. He sent away for the instructions from *Ranger Rick*.
2. Since he was in Cub Scouts, and the project looked like it was going to take some work, he recruited a few other Cubs to help.
3. They asked a lumber company to donate wood. The store agreed and gave them "rough-cut," unfinished pine.
4. They cut the wood into pieces and made 5 boxes.
5. Hunter's mother brought a ladder and nailed the boxes up on the side of North Hall.

SOURCE

Short Story

The Earth Game

By
Pam Conrad

Illustrated by
Diane Goode

Not very long ago, in a meadow not too far from here, some children found a ball of twine lying in the grass.

"Watch me," called the oldest girl. And she tied the end of the string to her finger and tossed the ball in the air.

Her brother caught it and wrapped the string around his own finger. Then he pitched it across to his friend. The twine unwound just enough as it sailed through the air. His friend caught the ball, wrapped the string around his thumb, and threw it over to someone else.

After many tosses back and forth, the ball had unwound to just a loose end, and the smallest child wound that around his finger. And there they were, joined in a circle by the twine that wove a net at their center.

"Now look," said the oldest girl, and she wiggled her finger.

"I felt that!" said her brother.

"So did I," said his friend.

And standing very still, one by one, they each wiggled a finger until they could feel the twine move with even the gentlest tug.

"Now, let's be the Earth," said the girl. She closed her eyes, and her voice lifted over the meadow. "I am a jungle in Africa, and someone is shooting an elephant for his tusks." She moved her finger. They all felt the tug and grew sad.

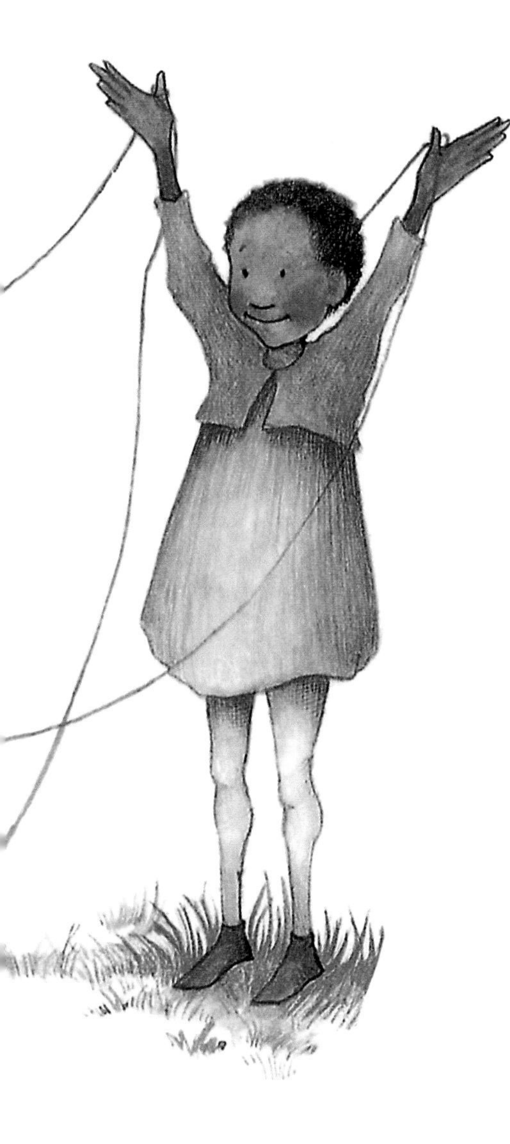

"I'm the Arctic Ocean," said her brother, "and an oil tanker is hitting an iceberg and spilling oil over me. Soon all the birds will be black and slick and won't fly anymore." He tugged, and they were silent.

"I am a big city, and no one can see the stars in the sky because the air is thick with smoke and fumes from my factories." The gentle tug passed around them.

"I was once a farm, but the sunflowers and rows of corn are gone. Today I am a mall." They each felt the sad tug.

They stopped tugging. It was as though a thick cloud had passed before the sun and darkened their day. It was very still, except for a bird whizzing by over their heads.

Then the smallest boy smiled. He moved his finger. "I'm a town, and in a backyard somebody's putting out seed for the winter birds." He tugged again, and their faces lit up.

"Yes!" The tallest girl raised her hands, and the pull was felt by all. "I'm a highway, and people are walking alongside me, picking up bottles and cans for recycling." She wiggled her fingers and laughed, and they could all feel it.

"I'm a neighborhood, and people are planting trees along my concrete sidewalks."

"I am an ocean, and fishermen are freeing the dolphins from their nets."

"I'm a herd of wild mustangs, and someone has given me land and turned me loose."

"I'm a lonely country road, and somebody's painting my mailbox red."

They all laughed. Then they raised their hands, lifting the net of twine higher and higher. They could feel the certain pull of all the things people could do to make a better world.

And that is how—not too long ago, in a meadow not very far from here—a ball of twine was the beginning of the Earth game.

Glossary

affect
to cause something to happen
A sad movie can **affect** you and make you cry.

bitter
sharp, stinging
The **bitter** wind stings our faces.

blew
moved by air
When I **blew** my whistle, it made a loud sound.

blossom
a flower
The bee sat on a large red **blossom.**

blossom

blowhole
the breathing hole of a whale on top of its head
A whale blows air out of its **blowhole.**

calves
young whales
We saw a mother whale swimming with her **calves.**

clover
a plant with three leaves and small flowers that grows low on the ground
Clover grows in our yard and smells sweet.

clover

conservation
protection from harm or loss
If we all practice **conservation** and do not cut down too many trees, we will save our forests.

disappearing
going out of sight
The school bus is **disappearing** around the corner.

dive
to go into the water with your head first
I close my eyes when I **dive** into the water.

honeycomb

drifts
piles of snow
The **drifts** were as high as the cars.

endangered
in danger of dying out
If we protect wolves, they will not become **endangered**.

extinction
dying out
The **extinction** of the dinosaurs took place a long time ago.

frozen
turned into ice
Children skate on the **frozen** lake.

honeycombs
places in the hive where bees store their honey
The **honeycombs** are the color of gold.

dive

hoot
to make a noise like an owl

The owl begins to **hoot** at night.

howl
to make a noise like the cry of a wolf

We heard the dog **howl** when he hurt his paw.

howling
a noise like the cry of a wolf

The **howling** of the wind kept us awake.

humpback
a black-and-white whale with a humplike fin

The **humpback** whale has a hump on its back that is made of fat.

injured
hurt

We knew the little bird was **injured** because it could not fly.

pollen
a fine yellow powder on flowers

Bees carry **pollen** from flower to flower.

preventing
stopping from happening

We are **preventing** milk from turning sour by keeping it cold.

protect
to keep safe

Helmets **protect** our heads when we ride our bikes.

rescued
saved from danger

The fire fighters **rescued** the people from the burning house.

scarce
hard to find

Diamonds are very **scarce** in most parts of the world.

scolded
told someone that something is wrong in an angry way

Mom **scolded** me for not doing my homework.

scream
a loud, scared cry

You might let out a **scream** when you watch a scary movie.

shouts
loud calls

Their **shouts** can be heard from far away.

whales

shrieked
gave a sudden, loud, sharp cry

I **shrieked** when I saw the snake on the path.

skidded
slid sideways

The car **skidded** on the icy road.

spout
wet air like fog

You can see the whale's **spout** when it blows air out of its blowhole.

survive
to stay alive

Animals need food to **survive.**

swarmed
moved around together in a large group

The bees **swarmed** around the farmer but did not sting him.

swirling
moving around in circles

The leaves were **swirling** in the wind.

trapped
not able to leave or escape

When they locked the door, the boy was **trapped** in the room.

vanishing
going out of sight suddenly

The plane was **vanishing** behind a cloud in the sky.

whales
very large animals that live in the ocean

Some **whales** are the biggest animals alive.

Authors and Illustrators

Pam Conrad pages 132–137

When Pam Conrad was seven years old, she had the chicken pox. Her mother got her paper and colored pencils for drawing. Instead, Pam started to write. Soon she was entering writing contests—and winning! Some of Conrad's other books are *The Tub People* and *Molly and the Strawberry Day*.

Kristine L. Franklin
pages 96–117

Kristine L. Franklin has traveled all over the world and lived in many places. She lived for a while in Costa Rica, the country where *When the Monkeys Came Back* takes place. This author likes writing books that tell about life outside the United States. Two other books by Franklin are *The Old, Old Man and the Very Little Boy* and *The Shepherd Boy*.

John Himmelman pages 50–67

One morning, John Himmelman was on a ship near Provincetown, Massachusetts. A whale swam right over to the ship. A scientist on board told the author that, just one year before, this same whale had been rescued from a net. That whale was the real Ibis! Seeing her close up made Himmelman want to write about this whale. *Montague on the High Seas* and *Simpson Snail Sings* are two other books by Himmelman.

Alexandra Wright pages 70–89

Alexandra Wright wrote *Will We Miss Them? Endangered Species* when she was in the sixth grade! She wrote this book because she was worried about what was happening to some animals. She hoped that if more kids knew about this problem they would want to help. This young author has written two more books about animals, *Can We Be Friends?* and *At Home in the Tidepool.*

Acknowledgments

Grateful acknowledgment is made to the following sources for permission to reprint from previously published material. The publisher has made diligent efforts to trace the ownership of all copyrighted material in this volume and believes that all necessary permissions have been secured. If any errors or omissions have inadvertently been made, proper corrections will gladly be made in future editions.

Cover: Fran Lee.

Interior: "The Old Ladies Who Liked Cats" from THE OLD LADIES WHO LIKED CATS by Carol Greene, illustrated by Loretta Krupinski. Text copyright © 1991 by Carol Greene. Illustrations copyright © 1991 by Loretta Krupinski. Reprinted by permission of HarperCollins Publishers.

Selections and cover from THE MAGIC SCHOOL BUS ON THE OCEAN FLOOR by Joanna Cole, illustrated by Bruce Degen. Text copyright © 1992 by Joanna Cole. Illustrations copyright © 1992 by Bruce Degen. Reprinted by permission of Scholastic Inc. THE MAGIC SCHOOL BUS is a registered trademark of Scholastic Inc.

"Balto, The Dog Who Saved Nome" from FIVE TRUE DOG STORIES by Margaret Davidson. Text copyright © 1977 by Margaret Davidson. Published by Scholastic Inc. Illustrations for this version by Cathie Bleck. Illustrations copyright © 1996 by Scholastic Inc.

Text of "Puppygarten Star" from the September 1994 issue of *Kid City* Magazine. Copyright © 1994 by Children's Television Workshop (New York, NY). All rights reserved. Photographs by Justin Sutcliffe from ROSIE: A VISITING DOG'S STORY by Stephanie Calmenson. Photographs copyright © 1994 by Justin Sutcliffe. Reprinted by permission of Clarion Books/Houghton Mifflin Co. All rights reserved.

"Ibis: A True Whale Story" from IBIS: A TRUE WHALE STORY by John Himmelman. Copyright © 1990 by John Himmelman. Reprinted by permission of Scholastic Inc.

Selections and cover from WILL WE MISS THEM? ENDANGERED SPECIES by Alexandra Wright, illustrated by Marshall Peck III. Copyright © 1992 by Charlesbridge Publishing. Reprinted by permission of Charlesbridge Publishing.

"When the Monkeys Came Back" from WHEN THE MONKEYS CAME BACK by Kristine L. Franklin, illustrated by Robert Roth. Text copyright © 1994 by Kristine L. Franklin. Illustrations copyright © 1994 by Robert Roth. Reprinted by arrangement with Atheneum Books for Young Readers, Simon & Schuster Children's Publishing Division.

"In the Jungle" and cover from ANIMAZE! by Wendy Madgwick, illustrated by Lorna Hussey. Text copyright © 1992 by Wendy Madgwick. Illustrations copyright © 1992 by Lorna Hussey. Reprinted by permission of Alfred A. Knopf, Inc.

Material from KID HEROES OF THE ENVIRONMENT ($4.95) © 1991, by The EarthWorks Group. Cover illustration by Steve Purcell. Published by EarthWorks Press, Berkeley, CA. Used with permission.

"The Earth Game" by Pam Conrad, illustrated by Diane Goode. Text copyright © 1993 by Pam Conrad. Illustrations copyright © 1993 by Diane Goode. Originally published in THE BIG BOOK FOR OUR PLANET, edited by Ann Durell, Jean Craighead George, and Katherine Paterson, published by Dutton Children's Books, 1993. Used by permission of Maria Carvainis Agency, Inc. and Diane Goode. All rights reserved.

Cover from ANTARCTICA by Helen Cowcher. Illustration copyright © 1990 by Helen Cowcher. Published by Farrar, Strauss & Giroux.

Cover from KITTEN CARE AND CRITTERS, TOO! by Judy Petersen-Fleming and Bill Fleming, photographs by Debra Reingold-Reiss. Photographs copyright © by Darryl Bush/Marine World Africa U.S.A., Vallejo, CA. Published by Tambourine Books, a division of William Morrow & Company, Inc.

Cover from A PLACE FOR GRACE by Jean Davies Okimoto, illustrated by Doug Keith. Illustration copyright © 1993 by Doug Keith. Published by Sasquatch Books.

Cover from WHO EATS WHAT? FOOD CHAINS AND FOOD WEBS by Patricia Lauber, illustrated by Holly Keller. Illustration copyright © 1995 by Holly Keller. Published by HarperCollins Children's Books, a division of HarperCollins Publishers.

Photography and Illustration Credits

Selection Opener Photographs by David S. Waitz Photography/Alleycat Design, Inc.

Photos: p. 2 tl: © Luis Rosendo/FPG International Corp.; cr: © Dick Sawicki/FPG International Corp.; bl: © Bill Losh/FPG International Corp.;. p. 3 bl: A. Schmidecker/ FPG International Corp.; br: © Walter P. Calahan for Scholastic Inc. p. 45 © Ana Esperanza Nance for Scholastic Inc. pp. 68-69 © Center for Coastal Studies, Provincetown, MA except for p. 68 cl: Larry Maglott for Scholastic Inc. p. 90 cl, bl: © Walter P. Calahan for Scholastic Inc.; tr: © Martin Simon for Scholastic Inc. p. 91 c: © Walter P. Calahan for Scholastic Inc. p. 92 tr: © Walter P. Calahan for Scholastic Inc.; cl: © Martin Simon for Scholastic Inc. pp. 92-93 br: © Walter P. Calahan for Scholastic Inc. p. 93 tr: © Walter P. Calahan for Scholastic Inc.; cr, cl: © Martin Simon for Scholastic Inc. p. 138 br: © Craig Tuttle/The Stock Market; c: © Dave Davis/FPG International Corp. p. 139 bl: © Blair Seitz/Photo Researchers, Inc.; tr: © Brownie Harris/The Stock Market. p. 141 tc: © Francois Gohier/Photo Researchers, Inc. p. 142 bl: © Sarah Conrad. p. 143 bl: © John Himmelmann; br: © Courtesy of Alexandra Wright.

Illustrations: pp. 2-3: Jackie Snider; pp. 8-9: Fran Lee; pp. 30-45: Cathie Bleck; pp. 48-49, 94-95: Fran Lee; pp. 132-137: Drew Brook-Cormack, border art.